THE FOURTH ONE AND ONLY COLOURING BOOK FOR ADULTS

The Fourth One And Only Colouring Book For Adults

ISBN: 978-1-907912-97-9

First published in English by Phoenix Yard Books Ltd, 2016

Phoenix Yard Books
Phoenix Yard
65 King's Cross Road
London WC1X 9LW

1 3 5 7 9 10 8 6 4 2

A CIP catalogue record for this book is available from the British Library

Printed in Malaysia

www.phoenixyardbooks.com

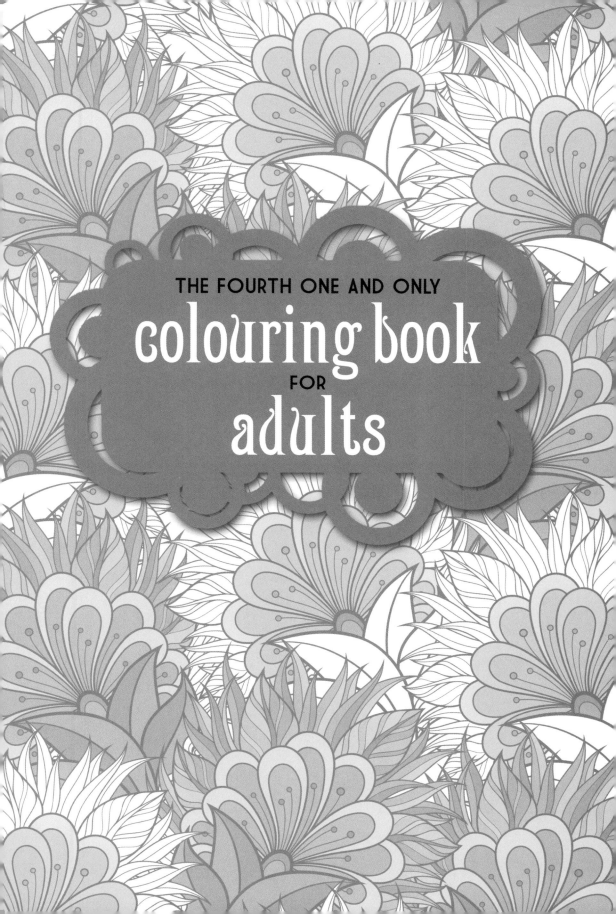

THE FOURTH ONE AND ONLY
colouring book
FOR
adults

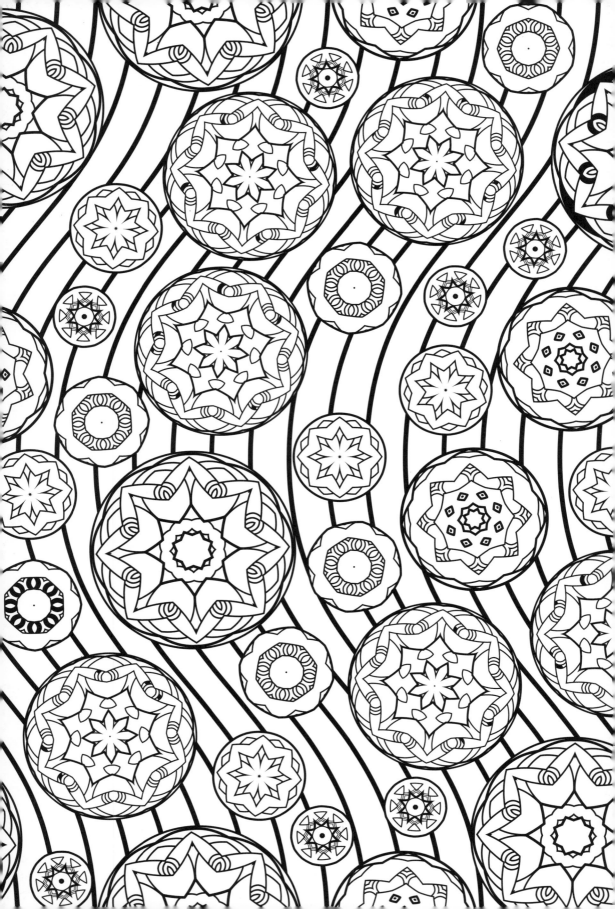

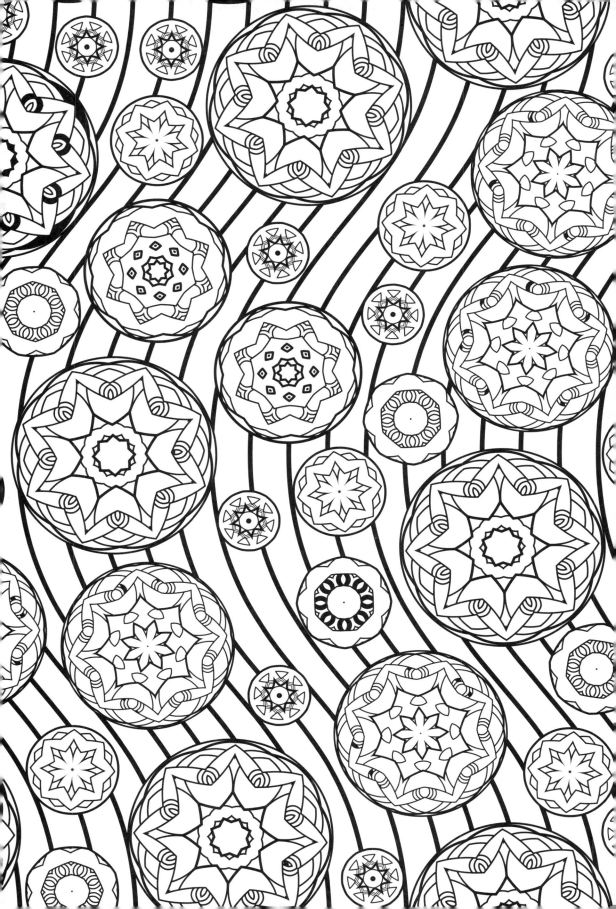

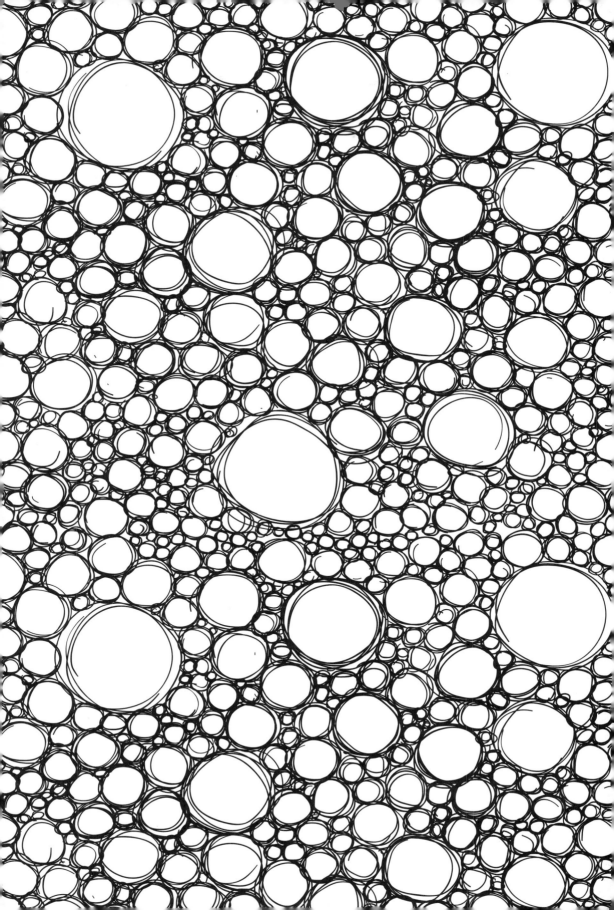

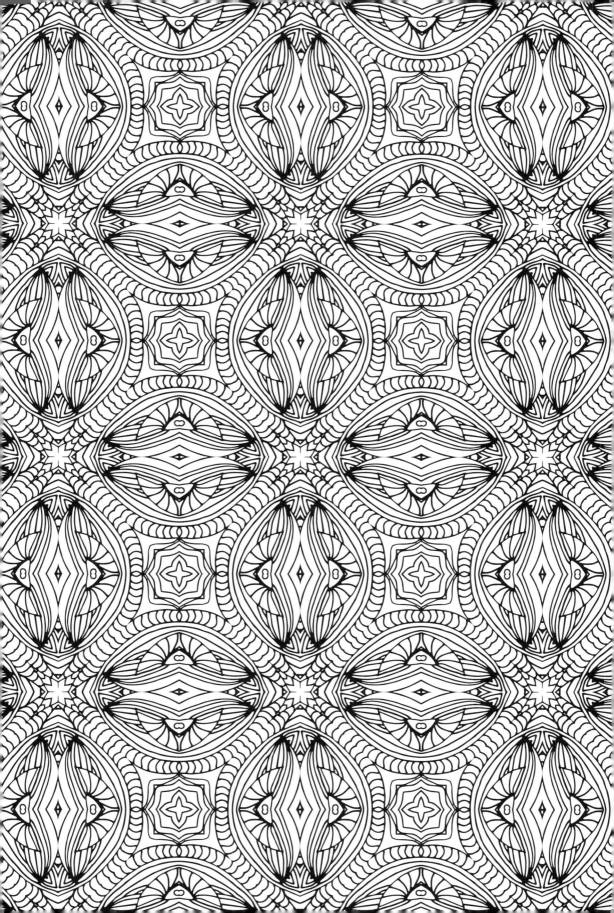

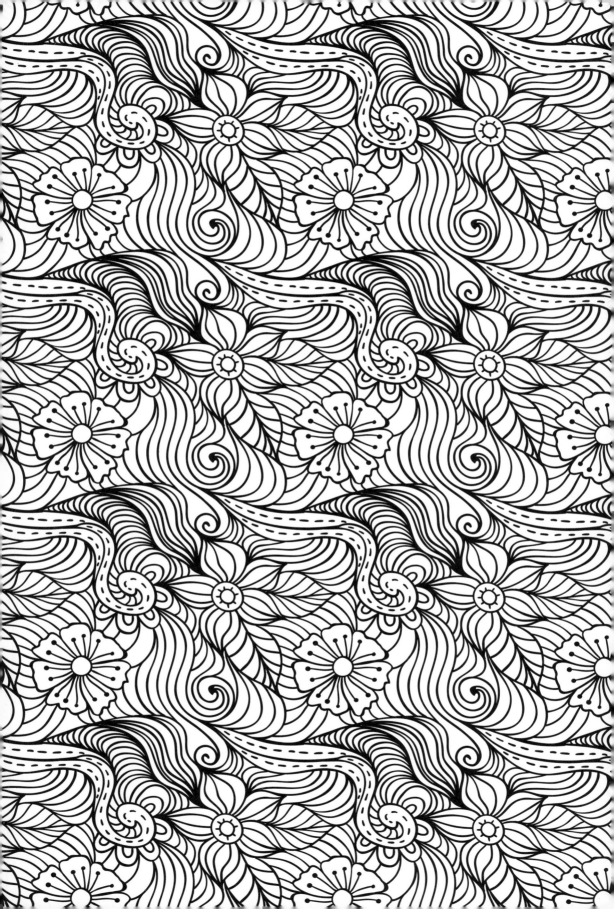

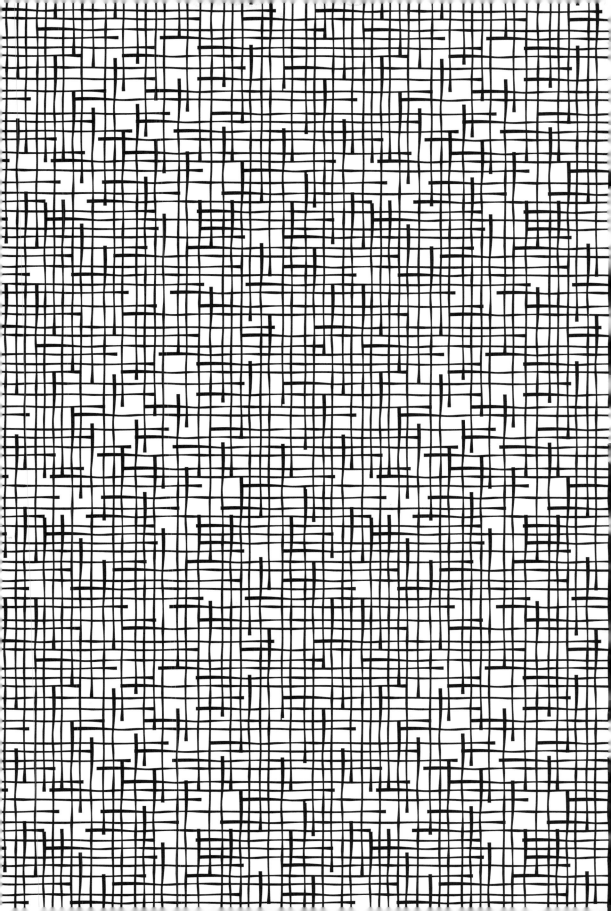

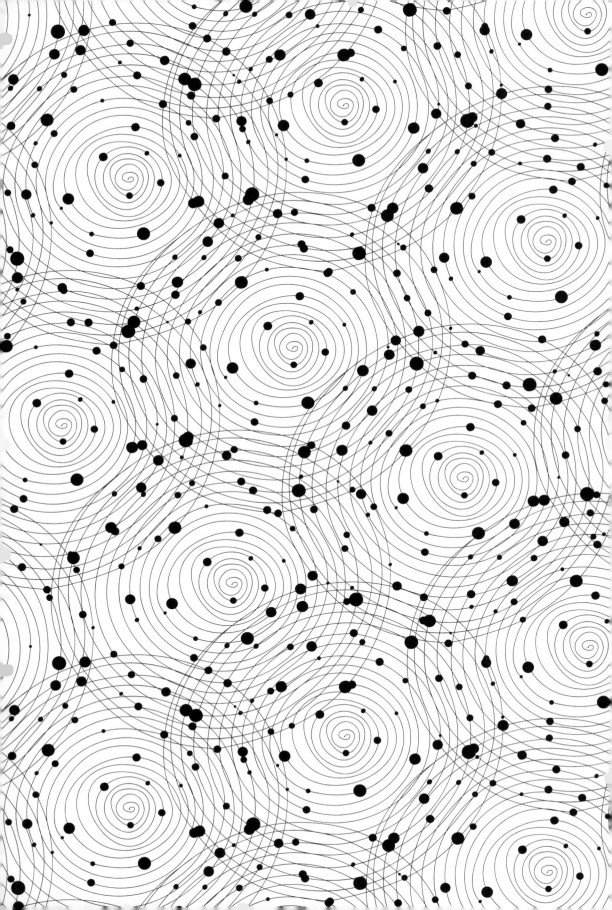